More True Cat Stories

A Dolch Classic Basic Reading Book

by Marguerite P. Dolch

illustrated by Gary Undercuffler

The Basic Reading Books

The Basic Reading Books are fun reading books that fill the need for easy-to-read stories for the primary grades. The interest appeal of these true stories will encourage independent reading at the early reading levels.

The stories focus on the 95 Common Nouns and the Dolch 220 Basic Sight Vocabulary. Beyond these simple lists, the books use about two or three new words per page.

This series was prepared under the direction and supervision of Edward W. Dolch, Ph.D.

This series was revised under the direction and supervision of Eleanor Dolch LaRoy and the Dolch Family Trust.

SRA/McGraw-Hill

A Division of The **McGraw·Hill** Companies

Printed in the United States of America.

Send all inquiries to:
SRA/McGraw-Hill
250 Old Wilson Bridge Road, Suite 310
Worthington, OH 43085

ISBN 0-02-830806-9

2 3 4 5 6 7 8 9 0 QST 04 03 02 01 00 99

Table of Contents

Minnie and Matt

Minnie and Matt lived with Mrs. Garza. Minnie was a mother cat with three babies. The mother cat had a box under the kitchen table where her babies had a nice warm bed.

Matt was a dog. He and Minnie were good friends. Every day Matt went into the kitchen and looked into the box where the kittens slept. He never tried to hurt the kittens because Matt was a kind dog.

The three kittens had just opened their eyes. They crawled around in their box. Minnie knew that it was time for her kittens to have a new place to sleep.

The mother cat went all over the house. She went to the living room and jumped up into a chair that was nice and soft. Minnie thought the chair would be a nice place for her babies.

Mrs. Garza went into the room. "How are you, Minnie?" she said. "I am going to sit down in that chair."

Minnie knew that this was no place for her babies.

Minnie went into a bedroom. She jumped up on the bed. The bed was a nice, soft place for her kittens. Minnie was a little cat. She looked over the side of the bed. The floor was far down. This would never do. Her little babies would fall off the bed and get hurt.

Minnie jumped off the bed. She went around the bedroom. At last she got to a closet, and the closet door was open. Minnie went into the closet.

There in the dark, warm closet was a soft rug in a corner. This was just the place for her babies.

Minnie went back to her box in the kitchen. The kittens were hungry. After Minnie had fed them, she picked up one kitten in her mouth. She took the kitten out of the box and tried to carry it across the kitchen floor.

But Minnie was a little cat. The kitten was too big for her to carry. Minnie did not know what to do. She sat beside her kitten for a long time.

At last Minnie went to find Matt. The dog was asleep under a living room table.

Somehow Minnie told Matt that she needed help. She wanted him to go to the kitchen. The dog and the cat went to the kitchen. Minnie sat down beside the little kitten that was on the kitchen floor.

The mother cat picked up the kitten in her mouth and showed Matt how to carry it. She pushed the kitten to Matt. He did not understand.

Minnie took Matt to the bedroom. She showed him the nice soft rug in the closet. She tried to tell Matt that this rug would be a good place for her kittens.

Minnie and Matt went back to the kitchen. Again Minnie picked up the kitten in her mouth and showed Matt how to carry it. This time Matt understood. He picked up the kitten in his mouth very carefully. He did not hurt it.

Minnie ran to the bedroom. This time Matt understood. He carried the kitten into the bedroom and put it on the soft rug in the closet.

One at a time, the kind dog carried the kittens into the bedroom and put them in the closet. Minnie was very happy in her new home.

As the kittens grew bigger, Minnie sometimes wanted another place for her family. Each time she got Matt. Matt understood. He would pick up a kitten in his mouth and carry it to the place Minnie had picked out for her family.

When all three kittens were in the new place, Matt would sit beside Minnie and wag his tail. Maybe Matt was saying, "See what a smart dog I am. I can look after baby kittens, too."

Firehouse No. 6

All was quiet in Firehouse No. 6. It was a hot day and the big doors were open. Some of the firefighters were playing games. Some of the firefighters were taking a nap. And the pet bulldog, Red, was asleep in his box.

At this time, Sam thought he would visit Firehouse No. 6. Sam was a big, striped cat. He was a proud cat, and he walked with his tail held high.

Sam rubbed the legs of two men sitting by the door. Sam purred and said meow. The men laughed, and one man said, "You may come in and look around, but Red will soon run you out."

Sam walked into Firehouse No. 6. The big cat climbed up on the fire engine. He smelled it. He liked the smell.

Soon Sam climbed down from the fire engine. He went up some stairs to the place where the firefighters slept. Then, Sam went to sleep on one of the beds.

Red, the bulldog, was still asleep. All that hot afternoon, Sam, the striped cat, slept on the bed of one of the firefighters. And, Red, the bulldog, slept in his box.

Slowly Red opened his eyes. Then suddenly he was awake. Red smelled a cat. He jumped out of his box. That cat had been walking around his firehouse. That cat had been on his fire engine. That cat had walked up the stairs and slept in a bed.

Red did not want a cat in Firehouse No. 6. He was going to get that cat.

In the firehouse, there is a big, brass pole that goes from the upstairs to the downstairs. When the fire alarm rings, the people who are upstairs slide down the pole. It is the quickest way for them to get downstairs and onto the fire engine. This pole was right beside the bed where Sam was sleeping.

Sam woke up suddenly. He saw that a big bulldog was about to get him. There was only one way the cat could get away from the dog—Sam jumped for the brass pole.

This pole was not a like a tree. Sam could not hold onto the pole with his claws, so Sam put his paws around the pole and held on. He went down the pole just like a firefighter.

Sam could hear Red growling. As soon as Sam hit the floor, he ran to the fire engine. He jumped up on the seat where the big dog could not get him.

Some of the firefighters had seen Sam slide down the pole. They were laughing and telling the other firefighters how the cat got away from Red because the dog could not slide down the brass pole.

The firefighters said that a cat who was smart enough to get away from Red could stay in the firehouse.

Sam had learned two things. One: a dog cannot slide down a brass pole. Two: a smart cat can slide down a brass pole, and it is a lot of fun.

From that day, Sam has lived at Firehouse No. 6. He likes to sleep on the bed near the brass pole. Whenever the fire alarm rings, Sam is the first one to slide down the pole. He sits on the fire engine and goes to the fire.

Red is now an old dog. He lives on a farm now and sleeps in the sun. Sometimes he thinks about Firehouse No. 6 and the cat he could never catch.

The Love of David

David was a little, black kitten. David went to live in a house with two other cats. One cat was brown and white and was named Robert. The other cat was a very big, gray cat named Heathcliff.

The two big cats would have nothing to do with the kitten. When David wanted to play, the two big cats would go outdoors and hide under the bushes.

One day David was very brave. He went outdoors, too. Heathcliff saw him and chased him under a doghouse in the backyard. There was just enough room for the kitten to crawl under it.

David stayed under the doghouse, while Heathcliff walked around the doghouse.

At last the big cat went away and sat on the grass looking at the doghouse. He seemed to say, "Little kitten, you do as I tell you, or I will not let you come out from under the doghouse."

Slowly David crawled out from under the doghouse. He went over to the big cat and touched his nose.

From that day on, Heathcliff was David's friend. David followed Heathcliff everywhere. The big cat taught David everything a kitten should know.

Heathcliff taught David bird watching and mouse catching. He taught him how to fight and how to hide from danger. He even let David sleep with him in his basket.

Even Robert became David's friend. Robert sometimes let David play with his tail. But David loved the big cat Heathcliff best.

Heathcliff and David ate together and played together. They played all over the house and yard. Heathcliff even washed David as a mother cat washes her kitten. David was a happy little kitten.

One day Heathcliff went out on the road. He did not see the car that was coming so fast. The car hit Heathcliff. He was taken to a doctor, but the doctor could not save him.

David hunted all over the house. He cried and called for his friend, but Heathcliff did not come. Then, David hunted all over the yard, and Robert hunted with him. They could not find Heathcliff.

For a long week, the two cats hunted for their friend. But they could not find him.

At last Robert understood that Heathcliff was gone. Robert must have been sorry for the little kitten because he began to wash David's fur and play with him.

David grew to be a big cat. Sometimes he would hunt in the house and in the yard as if he were looking for Heathcliff.

David made friends with all the other cats in the neighborhood. There was a broken window in the cellar of the house where he lived. And every night the neighborhood cats went through the broken

window and visited with David. But David never forgot Heathcliff.

One evening David took a big, gray cat into the living room. He showed the big, gray cat the box of toys that he and Heathcliff had played with. But the big cat did not know how to play with a ball or a piece of string. This big, gray cat was not Heathcliff.

The big cat ran into the cellar and out the broken window. David followed him into the cellar and sat by the broken window all night.

Joe Bulldozer

What are you to do when a cat wants to
live with you? It was only a yellow kitten.
Every day it looked in at the glass door to
the dining room.

Every day the Man-of-the-House took the yellow kitten back to the butcher in the city. The yellow kitten lived with three cats who caught mice that tried to get into the butcher shop.

Every day the butcher gave the cats and the yellow kitten nice meat. But the yellow kitten did not want to live in a butcher shop.

Every evening when the Man-of-the-House got home, there was a yellow kitten looking in at the glass door to the dining room.

"I thought you took the yellow kitten back to the butcher shop," said the Woman-of-the-House.

"I did," said the Man-of-the-House. "But the yellow kitten will not stay with the butcher.

The Woman-of-the-House took the yellow kitten back to the butcher.

"That little Joe will not stay with me," said the butcher. "I have three cats, and if you would like to have the yellow kitten, you may keep him."

"I have two cats," said the Woman-of-the-House. "But if Joe, the yellow kitten, wants to stay with me, I will keep him."

The Woman-of-the-House went home. In a little while, there was Joe, the yellow kitten, looking in at the glass door to the dining room.

"If you can get along with my two cats, you may stay with me," said the Woman-of-the-House.

One of the cats, whose name was Barney, did not like Joe. He tried to run Joe off, but Joe always came back. Every night there was Joe looking in at the glass door of the dining room.

At last Joe was let into the house to eat his supper with the other cats. Joe was happy in his home at last.

The Man-of-the-House laughed and said, "Joe certainly bulldozed his way into our house."

And that is how Joe Bulldozer got his name.

Joe Bulldozer grew into a beautiful cat. One day Joe Bulldozer went into the kitchen carrying something in his mouth as a mother cat carries a kitten.

Very carefully Joe laid the baby rabbit at the feet of the Man-of-the-House. Then, Joe went out again and carried in another baby rabbit.

The Man-of-the-House put the baby rabbits into a little box and carried them out into the garden. He thought that the mother rabbit would find them and take care of them.

Joe would never hurt any little animals. Joe made friends with all the neighbors—that is, with all the neighbors who liked cats. He seemed to know when anyone was going to have a party. Joe always liked to go to a party, for he liked cake very much.

Once, Joe was hit by a car. He crawled under some bushes, but the Man-of-the-House found him in the bushes and took him to a doctor. Joe was a very sick cat, but he got all right.

Then, Joe went to the city with his family. He lived in an apartment. Joe visited other apartments. Everyone loved the beautiful, yellow cat.

One day, the Woman-of-the-House brought home a new kitten. Joe would not stay at home with the new kitten. He bulldozed his way into another apartment where there were no kittens.

Sometimes Joe back went to visit the Woman-of-the-House. She gave him a piece of cake, and Joe purred his loud, loud purr. When the yellow cat finished his cake, he asked to be let out. Then, Joe Bulldozer went back to his new home.

The Cat Dance

There was a beautiful dancer who was afraid of cats. When she was a little girl, she had played with a cat. She hurt the cat, so the cat scratched her. After that, she was afraid of all cats.

When the little girl, whose name was Fanny, grew up, she became a ballet dancer. She was asked to dance in a ballet in which she would be a white cat.

The ballet was about a Chinese princess who fell in love with a prince who loved cats. The prince would not even look at the beautiful princess. He liked cats more than he liked any person.

The princess went to a man of magic and asked him how she could win the love of the prince.

The man of magic changed the princess into a white cat. The prince thought this white cat was the most beautiful white cat he had ever seen. He loved her very much.

The man of magic did not want the prince to love a cat more than he would a person. So the man of magic made the white cat do all the naughty things that cats do. It spit at the prince. It scratched the prince. Soon the prince did not like the white cat. He did not like any cats.

Then, the man of magic changed the white cat back into the beautiful princess. The prince fell in love with her, and they were married.

That is the story of the ballet that was danced to beautiful music. In the dance, Fanny, the ballet dancer, had to act like a cat.

If you have watched a cat, you know how a cat acts. A cat walks with its tail held high when it is happy. A cat purrs and rubs against those it likes. When a cat is angry, it lifts its back. It spits and scratches. When a cat plays with a ball, it jumps high and hits the ball with its paws.

Fanny wanted the movements of her dance to be like the movements of a real cat.

"I had to buy a white cat," said Fanny. "I went to a pet shop and got a little, white kitten."

Fanny was afraid every time she put her hand on that white kitten, but she took it home. The white kitten loved Fanny and played around the house.

Fanny watched the kitten and tried to move like the kitten did.

As the kitten grew to be a cat, Fanny was no longer afraid of all cats. She learned to act just like a cat. She learned to try to catch a mouse, just like a cat. She learned to play with a ball. She learned to sleep all curled up, just like a cat.

At last, it was the first night to dance the ballet. There was beautiful music. The curtain went up.

The stage was a beautiful Chinese garden. The princess was on the stage with the man of magic. Slowly, the princess danced as if she were changed into a white cat.

The white cat stretched and ran about the stage. It rubbed against the man of magic to show how happy it was.

When the prince went on the stage, you could tell that he loved the white cat. But the man of magic made the white cat very naughty and very wild. It spit at the prince and scratched him. The prince did not like the white cat.

Then, the man of magic changed the white cat back into the princess, and everyone was happy.

Fanny danced a beautiful cat dance. When the curtain went down, the audience clapped and clapped. Fanny went in front of the curtain with her own white cat in her arms. She bowed to the audience.

Tomcat

Tomcat was long and thin. He had been in so many fights that pieces of his black fur had been torn away. His ears had been torn, and one eye was almost closed because another cat had scratched him in the face.

Tomcat lived in Farmer Brown's barn. He caught the mice that wanted to eat the corn. Farmer Brown milked the cows morning and night. He always left a dish of milk in the barn for Tomcat.

Only after Farmer Brown carried the milk into the house would Tomcat come out of his hiding place. Tomcat was afraid of people. He would look all around to see that no one was in the barn. Then, he would drink his milk.

No one had ever petted Tomcat, and I think no one had ever heard Tomcat purr.

Mrs. Brown's sister lived on a farm about three miles away. One day the sister went to see Mrs. Brown. She took her beautiful cat Molly with her.

"I will have to go away from home for a few weeks," said Mrs. Brown's sister. "I am afraid to leave Molly at home. She is going to have kittens very soon."

"I will take good care of Molly," said Mrs. Brown. "When you get home from your trip, I will bring her to you."

"Molly's kittens will be born any day," said Mrs. Brown's sister.

"We must fix Molly a box in the kitchen so that she will have a nice home for her family," said Mrs. Brown.

But Molly did not like the box in the kitchen. She went out into the barn. She made herself a nest in the hay. And then she saw Tomcat.

Molly loved Tomcat as soon as she saw him. For the first time in Tomcat's life another cat loved him. Tomcat was very happy. He caught mice and took them to Molly, and Farmer Brown left two dishes of milk.

In two days, Molly's kittens were born.
Tomcat sat beside the nest and watched
Molly. If anyone came into the barn, he
would spit and growl. He was going to look
after Molly.

When the kittens were a week old,
Molly let Farmer Brown and Mrs. Brown see
that she had three kittens. Mrs. Brown
carried the kittens into the house and put
them in the box in the kitchen, but Molly did
not like the box in the kitchen.

One by one, the mother cat carried her
kittens back to the barn and put them in her
nest in the hay.

When the kittens were three weeks old, Mrs. Brown put Molly and her kittens in the car and took them to her sister's farm.

Molly stayed at the farm just one night. The next morning, Mrs. Brown saw Molly walking down the road carrying a kitten in her mouth. She was very tired and could hardly walk. Molly had walked over three miles and carried a kitten all the way.

Molly took the kitten to the barn and put it in her nest in the hay.

Pretty soon Mrs. Brown saw Molly and Tomcat come out of the barn. They walked down the road together.

The next morning, when Farmer Brown went to the barn to milk the cows, he saw Molly and Tomcat walking down the road.

Each cat was carrying a kitten in its mouth. The two cats were very tired. All night long they had been walking down the road.

They carried the kittens into the barn and put them in the nest in the hay. Then, Molly and Tomcat were happy again.

Tomcat sat by the nest and watched the kittens while Molly went to the house. He would not let the kittens get out of the nest.

Sometimes Molly would take the kittens to the house to show them to Mrs. Brown.

When her sister came back from the city, Mrs. Brown told her the story of Molly and Tomcat.

Then, her sister said, "I do not want to take Molly away from Tomcat. I will let you keep Molly. When the kittens are bigger, I will take them home."

"Now I have a family of cats in my barn," said Farmer Brown.

Molly and Tomcat went on living in Farmer Brown's barn. Every day Tomcat caught a mouse and took it to Molly. And every day Farmer Brown left two dishes of milk in the barn for the two cats.

Mother Cat

Lon Hai was a Siamese cat. She was very beautiful and had won a ribbon in a cat show.

Lon Hai was out in the yard with her owner, Mrs. Kelly. She always went walking on a leash like a dog, but this day Lon Hai got out of her collar and ran up a tree.

Lon Hai did not come down when Mrs. Kelly called. She kept going higher up in the tree. Then, Lon Hai looked down at Mrs. Kelly. Never had the little cat been so frightened. She held on to the tree with her sharp claws. She cried and cried as only a Siamese cat can cry. She was so frightened that she could not move.

Mrs. Kelly went to a neighbor and got a very tall ladder. She put the ladder up against the tree. Then, she climbed up the ladder and got Lon Hai out of the tree.

Lon Hai was still so frightened that she could not walk. She just lay on the ground and looked at Mrs. Kelly with big, blue eyes that seemed to say, "I will never climb a tree again."

When Lon Hai had her first kittens, she was a good mother. Lon Hai took good care of her kittens.

All the kittens but one went to new homes. This one little kitten was going to be sent a long way. It would have to grow bigger before it could be sent to its new home.

Lon Hai had such a good time with her little kitten. She washed her many times a day. She played games with the kitten all over the house.

Mrs. Kelly had broken her leg and had not been outdoors in a long time. One day she thought that she and Lon Hai should take a walk in the yard. She got the leash and they went for a walk. They did not take the kitten.

The kitten cried and cried. Mrs. Kelly was very sorry for the kitten.

"Poor little kitten," said Mrs. Kelly. "Do you want to go outdoors?"

Mrs. Kelly went back into the house and got the kitten. She carried it outdoors in her arms with Lon Hai walking beside her on the leash.

As soon as the kitten got outdoors, it jumped down to the grass. Away it went before Mrs. Kelly could catch it. The little kitten climbed up the tree.

Mrs. Kelly stood at the bottom of the tree and called and called. The little kitten looked down. Then, it became so frightened that it could not move. The kitten cried and cried. Lon Hai called to her kitten, but the kitten just cried and cried.

Then, Mrs. Kelly sat on the ground and took Lon Hai in her lap. She talked to the mother cat a long time.

"Lon Hai," she said, "listen to me very carefully. I have a broken leg. I cannot climb a ladder up the the tree to get your kitten. You are the only one that can get your kitten to come down from the top of the tree."

Mrs. Kelly took the leash off Lon Hai
and put her up in the tree. The cat
understood. Lon Hai began to climb the tree.
Very slowly she went up to where her kitten
was crying.

Mrs. Kelly could hear the Siamese cat
talk to her kitten. Soon the kitten stopped
crying.

Then, very slowly, Lon Hai began to go
down the tree. She showed her little kitten
how to get down from the top of the tree.
Very slowly, the kitten began to back down
the tree.

The little kitten would get frightened and stop. Then, Lon Hai would have to talk to her again. Lon Hai took a long time to get her kitten down the tree because the kitten was so frightened and would stop and cry.

Mrs. Kelly stood at the bottom of the tree. She did not say a word because she knew that she could not help. Lon Hai was very frightened, but Mrs. Kelly knew that she would try to save her kitten.

At last Mrs. Kelly could get the mother cat and her kitten. She took them in her arms and carried them into the house.

The poor little mother cat was so frightened that she could not stand. It was the kitten who washed the mother cat's face.

I think that the kitten was thanking her mother for getting her down from that tree.

Kathy's Christmas Present

Robert was thinking of Kathy. He was
sorry for her. She was lonesome. She lived in
the city and had no one to play with.

Kathy and her mother had stayed for
the summer on the farm where Robert lived.
When Kathy got to the farm, she was thin.
She had been very sick. On the farm, Kathy
began to get better. Soon she was laughing
and playing with Robert.

Robert and Kathy played with Shep, the
dog who took the sheep to the field. They
helped Robert's mother get eggs each day.
They played in the barn and watched
Robert's father milk the cows.

One day Robert and Kathy found Tabby
with four little kittens in a nest in the barn.
Kathy had never seen baby kittens. She ran
to her mother.

"Oh, Mother!" Kathy cried. "Tabby has
four babies, and they are so little that their
eyes are shut."

All summer Kathy watched the kittens grow. She would rather play with the kittens than play with Shep. She would rather play with the kittens than watch Robert's father milk the cows. It was a happy summer for Kathy.

Kathy and her mother had to go back to the city. Kathy cried because she did not want to leave the kittens.

Robert would have liked to give Kathy one of the kittens, but her mother said that the trip to the city was too long to take a kitten.

Robert watched the kittens playing in the barn. They were almost big cats. Tabby was teaching them to catch mice in the barn. It was getting cold and the mice were coming into the barn from the field.

Robert kept thinking of Kathy. She must be lonesome because she had no one to play with. She would be happy with a kitten. Then Robert had a wonderful thought. He would send Kathy a kitten for Christmas.

"Mother," asked Robert, "how can I give Kathy one of my kittens for Christmas?"

"Kathy lives in a big city," said Mother. "The city is far away from our farm. It would cost a lot of money to send a kitten because it would have to go on an airplane."

"There must be kittens in a big city," said Robert. "How can I get one for Kathy?"

"Do you remember my friend Rachel who came to visit last Christmas? Rachel is a police officer in the city," said Mother. "Maybe you could write to Rachel, and ask her to find a kitten for Kathy."

Robert wrote to Rachel.

Dear Rachel,
I have a friend named Kathy. She lives at 1523 Morning Street. She is lonesome because she has no one to play with.

I would like her to have a kitten. Will you please find her a kitten for a Christmas present?

Thank you.

Your friend,
Robert

P.S. Please put a red ribbon on the kitten.

Just before Christmas, a police officer
went to Kathy's house. She carried a box
with holes in it. Something meowed in the
box.

"Does a little girl named Kathy live
here?" asked Rachel. "I have a Christmas
present for her from a little boy named
Robert."

The police officer opened the box and took out a pretty kitten with a red ribbon on it.

"Robert asked Santa Claus to give you a pretty kitten to play with," said Rachel.

"Oh, oh, oh," cried Kathy, as she took the kitten in her arms. "I never knew that Santa Claus could be a police officer."

The Cowboys' Cat

One day the cowboys were sitting under a tree. Suddenly, a little, black kitten walked up to one of the men.

The kitten was very thin and very tired, as if it had come a long way. No one knew where the kitten had come from because there was not another house for ten miles.

"A black cat is good luck," said Jimmy, one of the cowboys.

"A black cat is bad luck," said another of the cowboys. "Mrs. Jones will never let a black cat stay on the ranch."

"The little kitten is hungry," said Jimmy. "I am sure that Mrs. Jones will feed it."

Jimmy took the little, black kitten over to the kitchen where Mrs. Jones cooked for the cowboys. Mrs. Jones did not like cats, but the kitten was so little and so thin that she said she would give it some milk.

"It can stay in my kitchen for a few days," said Mrs. Jones, "and then you must take it away."

"Mrs. Jones," said Jimmy, "don't you know that a black cat brings good luck?"

"I don't believe in such things," said Mrs. Jones.

But Mrs. Jones let the kitten stay in her kitchen. The kitten stayed in a corner where Jimmy had fixed a box for her. She did not get in the way.

The little, black kitten grew to be a black cat with not a bit of white on her.

All the cowboys loved Cat. They said that Cat brought good luck to the ranch.

Every week Mrs. Jones told the cowboys that Cat must go because she never liked cats. Then, Cat would catch a mouse in the kitchen, and Mrs. Jones would say that Cat could stay a little longer.

One day Cat went away from the ranch. The cowboys hunted for her, but they could not find her. No one knew where Cat had gone.

About a week later, the cowboys found Cat asleep in her box in the kitchen. They were very glad to see their pet again.

"Good luck has come back to the ranch," said Jimmy.

"Bad luck is what I call that cat," said Mrs. Jones, but she let Cat stay in her kitchen.

One morning Cat did not get out of her box. That evening when the cowboys went into the kitchen for supper, they looked in Cat's box—Cat had four little, black kittens.

Cat meowed as if to say, "See my pretty babies."

Mrs. Jones said, "One cat is bad enough, but I will not have five cats in my kitchen. That cat and her kittens must go."

The cowboys were very sad. They knew that they must take Cat and her kittens away.

Jimmy said, "I think that the McDonalds would like to have Cat and her kittens."

The McDonalds owned a ranch on the other side of the river, about ten miles away.

He put Cat and her kittens in a basket and tied the top down. Then, he rode over to the McDonalds' ranch.

Mrs. McDonald was glad to have Cat and her kittens. Her cat was getting old and did not catch mice.

Mrs. McDonald fixed a box on the porch. Then, Jimmy put Cat and her little, black kittens into the box.

Jimmy was very sad as he rode back across the river, but he was glad that Cat and her family had a good home. He knew the cowboys would miss the black cat and family of kittens.

This is not the end of the story.

Two days later, Mrs. Jones got up to make breakfast for the cowboys. She was going to put Cat's box away, but when she got to the box, she saw a very wet, black cat and four little, black kittens. They were all sound asleep.

Cat opened her eyes and looked up at Mrs. Jones. She meowed as if to say, "I brought my babies back home. Don't send me away again. Please let me stay."

Mrs. Jones dried Cat's fur and fed her warm milk.

When the cowboys came to breakfast, Mrs. Jones said, "Cat and her kittens are back home. I guess she will have to stay."

The cowboys could hardly believe that so little a cat could have walked all those miles and swum across the river, carrying a kitten in her mouth. She could only carry one kitten at a time. And the McDonald ranch was ten miles away on the other side of the river.

"I think Cat is the most brave little animal I have ever seen," said Jimmy.

a
about
across
act
acts
afraid
after
afternoon
again
against
airplane
alarm
all
almost
along
always
am
an
and
angry
animal
animals
another
any
anyone
apartment
apartments
are
arms
around
as
ask
asked
asleep
at
ate
audience

awake
away
babies
baby
back
backyard
bad
ball
ballet
barn
Barney
basket
be
beautiful
became
because
bed
bedroom
beds
been
before
began
believe
beside
best
better
big
bigger
bird
bit
black
blue
born
bottom
bowed
box
boy

brass
brave
breakfast
bring
brings
broken
brought
brown
Brown's
bulldog
bulldozed
Bulldozer
bushes
but
butcher
buy
by
cake
call
called
came
can
cannot
car
care
carefully
carried
carries
carry
carrying
cat
catch
catching
cats
cat's
caught
cellar

certainly
chair
changed
chased
Chinese
Christmas
city
clapped
claws
climb
climbed
closed
closet
cold
collar
come
coming
cooked
corn
corner
cost
could
cowboys
cowboys'
cows
crawl
crawled
cried
cry
crying
curled
curtain
dance
danced
dancer
danger
dark

David
David's
day
days
dear
did
dining
dish
dishes
do
doctor
does
dog
doghouse
don't
door
doors
down
downstairs
dried
drink
each
ears
eat
eggs
end
engine
enough
even
evening
ever
every
everyone
everything
everywhere
eye
eyes

face
fall
family
Fanny
far
farm
farmer
fast
father
fed
feed
feet
fell
few
field
fight
fights
find
finished
fire
firefighter
firefighters
firehouse
first
five
fix
fixed
floor
followed
for
forgot
found
four
friend
friends
frightened
from

front	Heathcliff	jumps
fun	held	just
fur	help	Kathy
games	helped	Kathy's
garden	her	keep
Garza	here	Kelly
gave	herself	kept
get	hide	kind
getting	hiding	kitchen
girl	high	kitten
give	higher	kittens
glad	him	knew
glass	his	know
go	hit	ladder
goes	hits	laid
going	hold	lap
gone	holes	last
good	home	later
got	homes	laughed
grass	hot	laughing
gray	house	lay
grew	how	learned
ground	hungry	leash
grow	hunt	leave
growl	hunted	left
growling	hurt	leg
guess	I	legs
had	if	let
hand	in	life
happy	into	lifts
hardly	is	like
has	it	liked
have	its	likes
hay	Jimmy	listen
he	Joe	little
hear	Jones	live
heard	jumped	lived

lives
living
Lon Hai
lonesome
long
longer
look
looked
looking
lost
lot
loud
love
loved
luck
made
magic
make
man
many
married
Matt
may
maybe
McDonald
McDonalds
McDonalds'
me
meat
men
meow
meowed
mice
miles
milk
milked
Minnie

miss
Molly
Molly's
money
more
morning
most
mother
mouse
mouth
move
movements
moves
Mrs.
much
music
must
my
name
named
nap
naughty
near
needed
neighbor
neighborhood
neighbors
nest
never
new
next
nice
night
no
nose
not
nothing

now
of
off
officer
oh
old
on
once
one
only
onto
open
opened
or
other
our
out
outdoors
over
own
owned
owner
party
paws
people
person
pet
petted
pick
picked
piece
pieces
place
play
played
playing
plays

please
pole
police
poor
porch
present
pretty
prince
princess
proud
purr
purred
purrs
pushed
put
quickest
quiet
rabbit
rabbits
Rachel
ran
ranch
rather
real
red
remember
ribbon
right
rings
river
road
Robert
Robert's
rode
room
rubbed
rubs

rug
run
sad
said
Sam
Santa Claus
sat
save
saw
say
saying
scratched
scratches
seat
see
seemed
seen
send
sent
sharp
she
sheep
Shep
shop
should
show
showed
shut
Siamese
sick
side
sister
sister's
sit
sits
sitting
sleep

sleeping
sleeps
slept
slide
slowly
smart
smell
smelled
so
soft
some
somehow
something
sometimes
soon
sorry
sound
spit
spits
stage
stairs
stand
start
stay
stayed
still
stood
stop
stopped
stories
story
street
stretched
string
striped
such
suddenly

summer
sun
supper
sure
swum
Tabby
table
tail
take
taken
taking
talk
talked
tall
taught
teaching
tell
telling
ten
than
thank
thanking
that
the
their
them
then
there
they
thin
things
think
thinking
thinks
this
those
thought

three
through
tied
time
times
tired
to
together
told
Tomcat
Tomcat's
too
took
top
torn
touched
toys
tree
tried
trip
true
try
two
under
understand
understood
up
upstairs
very
visit
visited
wag
walk
walked
walking
walks
want

wanted
wants
warm
was
wash
washed
washes
watch
watched
watching
way
we
week
weeks
went
were
wet
what
when
whenever
where
which
while
white
who
whose
why
wild
will
win
window
with
woke
woman
won
wonderful
word

would
write
wrote
yard
yellow
you
your